Algebra Experiments I
Exploring Linear Functions

Mary Jean Winter
Ronald J. Carlson

Dale Seymour Publications

We would like to thank the many teachers whose enthusiasm for the algebra experiments has encouraged us. Special thanks to the participants in the Exeter Conferences whose suggestions we gratefully acknowledge. Thank you also to our colleagues J. Shroyer, E. Carlson, and D. Winter, whose expertise, comments, and support were invaluable.

Managing Editor: Michael Kane
Project Editor: Mali Apple
Production: The Cowans
Design: Detta Penna
Cover Art: Rachel Gage

ISBN 0-201-81524-9
Printed in the United States of America
  14 15 16 17 18 06 05 04 03

1-800-321-3106
www.pearsonlearning.com

Contents

Introduction

The emphasis of every experiment in this collection is on the algebraic concepts of *line, slope, intercept, function, dependent variable,* and *independent variable.* We have intentionally omitted non-algebraic experiments (that is, non-functional relationships), such as the relation of height to arm span, that result in correlated points, even when the correlation is linear. The idea of a function and the words "is a linear function of" are reiterated in every experiment to build a basis for later work in algebra.

Most students, including those in accelerated algebra and college algebra, have difficulty when they first encounter problems involving linear functions. Often they are unable to solve problems such as the following:

- The price of a box of candy is a linear function of the net weight. If a $1\frac{1}{2}$-pound box costs $6.95 and a 4-pound box costs $16.45, how much would a 10-pound box cost?

- Assume that f is a linear function. If $f(2) = 7$ and $f(10) = -3$, find $f(5)$.

We believe the emphasis on linear functions may help students in later algebra. On the worksheets, students must explicitly state the functional relationship they have found. For example, in the Bouncing Ball experiment, if the line found is

$$y = 0.56x + 2,$$

the student must also write

$$\text{Bounce height} = 0.56 \times \text{Drop height} + 2.$$

The geometric experiments involving circles, angles, and cubes are different from the others in that there is, in theory, an exact answer. We have included them because of their unexpected popularity with students and teachers. They are also useful reminders that algebra and geometry are not isolated and disjoint subjects.

The First Experiment: A Class Project

Experiment 1, the Wave, is an ideal choice for introducing the experiments and will demonstrate how to obtain the data points and what to do with them once they are obtained.

First, discuss the mechanics. Record the data on the board after each "wave" is finished.

x number of people	y time

Record the class data. Have students copy the data onto the Points to Be Graphed table on their Collect the Data worksheets.

Graph the data. First, say: Now, we're going to graph the points. How should we measure the x and y units? After a discussion of scale, everyone should plot the points. When students notice that the points are almost collinear, have the class decide on a line through two of the points.

As a group, complete the Find the Equation worksheet. Find the equation of the line by finding its slope and intercept. Find both rational and decimal forms of the coefficients. Then complete the word equation:

$$\text{Wave time} = 3.2 \times \text{Number of people} + 0.6$$

Have students complete the follow-up questions on the Interpret the Data worksheet as an assignment.

The Second Experiment

Select any one of the other experiments as the second experiment. After introducing the experiment (see Teaching Notes), put a transparency of the Collect the Data worksheet on the overhead projector. Now is the time to introduce or to review the ideas of *independent variables* and *dependent variables*.

On the overhead, illustrate what is needed in the diagram, the written description, and the variable identifications. Emphasize that this portion of the page must be filled out before any data collection begins.

The Experiments and the NCTM *Standards*

The Curriculum and Evaluation Standards for School Mathematics (copyright 1989 by the National Council of Teachers of Mathematics) provides a vision of mathematical literacy for a changing world and establishes guidelines to help revise mathematics curriculum to reflect the new definition of mathematical literacy. *Algebra Experiments* reflects the same spirit and addresses the same aims by implementing the goals espoused in the *Standards:* life-long learning, mathematically literate workers, and opportunity for all students. Learning to value mathematics, becoming confident mathematical problem-solvers, and learning to communicate and reason mathematically are outcomes that can be attained through the use of the experiments.

Algebra Experiments provides a means of addressing the *Standards* at all levels: pre-algebra, integrated algebra, standard first- and second-year algebra, accelerated algebra, and pre-calculus. The summary of changes in instructional practices and topics listed below are taken from the *Standards*. They provided direction for the design of the experiments.

Changes in instructional practices in grades 9 to 12 mathematics require increased attention to the following goals:

- The active involvement of students in constructing and applying mathematical ideas
- Problem solving as a means as well as a goal of instruction
- The use of a variety of instructional formats (small groups, individual explorations, peer instruction, whole-class discussions, project work)
- The use of calculators and computers as tools for learning and doing mathematics
- Student communication of mathematical ideas orally and in writing

Changes in content in grades 9 to 12 mathematics require increased attention to the following topics:

- The use of real-world problems to motivate and apply algebraic theory
- Integration of function concepts across topics at all grade levels
- The connections among a problem situation, its model as a function in symbolic form, and the graph of that function
- Function equations expressed in standardized form as checks on the reasonableness of graphs produced by graphing utilities
- Functions that are constructed as models of real-world problems
- Statistical applications

Cooperative Learning and Individual Accountability

Algebra Experiments combines the benefits of cooperative learning and individual responsibility. There is student interaction, discussion, informal peer instruction, and shared ownership of a completed project, along with satisfaction and pride in a personally completed project and the individual's responsibility for understanding the mathematics and being able to complete the work involved.

Cooperative Learning

Most of the experiments require two people to successfully accomplish the collection of data. Even in those experiments one student could complete alone, two investigators help ensure accurate (consistent) data. During data collection, students will frequently make and share mathematical observations, such as: "Every time we add three, it goes up five. It must be linear."

After collecting data together, students have a natural interest in what their partners decide to do with their data: "Why did you pick those points, and not these?" "We shouldn't use that point, since the car nearly bounced." "It looks linear to me."

Informal peer teaching will often occur: "I didn't get that. Oh! I have the slope upside down!"

The Extension questions also produce discussions and conjectures to be challenged and defended: "I don't think that will happen. Let's try it and see." "Maybe it increases because . . ."

Individual Accountability

Each student should have a complete record of each experiment. Each should be able to describe in writing and with diagrams the exact nature of the experiment. Each should carry out the steps involved in finding a function and in answering the questions. It is important that each student write up the experiment completely, for purposes of evaluation, for possible inclusion in a portfolio, and as a record of accomplishment.

Evaluation and Assessment

The methods of evaluating student performance on an experiment and of assessing student understanding and learning will depend on how the experiment is used. An experiment might be used for enrichment, as an introduction, for motivation, for reinforcement, or as an adjunct to a mathematics course. An experiment may be marked as an assignment and returned, or it may be placed in a student's portfolio. Some suggestions for evaluation and examples of assessment questions follow.

Evaluating an Experiment: Marking Suggestions

Each experiment is divided naturally into three parts: Collect the Data (write-up and data collection), Find the Equation (determining a function representing the data), and Interpret the Data (responding to follow-up questions). How each part is counted depends on how the experiment is used. One method of evaluation, of course, is to give each part equal weight. Here are suggestions for awarding points to each part:

Collect the Data. If one assumes that the write-up, data collection, and graphing of the data are worth 10 points, the following is a possible allocation of credit:

> 2 points for a written description of the experiment
>
> 2 points for a diagram that shows the independent and dependent variables
>
> 2 points for identification of the variables and units

1 point for relevant identification and measurements of equipment

3 points for collecting and graphing the data

This distribution emphasizes the importance of understanding the experiment and being able to communicate, both visually and verbally, with others. The diagram may be minimal, but must clearly indicate the precise nature of the independent and dependent variables as well as the physical set-up. As long as the data produces points of a linear nature (which will be obvious from the graph), the precision of the data should not be unduly scrutinized. However, students should question an inconsistent point and perhaps repeat the experiment for that value of the independent variable. The physical limitations of the experiment should be also be respected; some values of the independent variable are too small or too large for the data to be meaningful.

Find the Equation. Give points for performing the algebraic tasks of finding the slope, the intercept, and the equation of the line. Give points for expressing the functional relationship, such as: Bounce height = $0.6 \times$ Drop height + 0.87.

Interpret the Data. Give points for the substitution (manipulation-type) questions. Give points for inferential questions, such as, "How would the graph change if . . . ?" or "How would the equation change if . . . ?" The responses to these semi-open questions can indicate the depth of understanding of the concepts and relationships.

Assessment Alternatives and the Experiments

The present thinking about mathematics assessment is that both the product and the process should be assessed. The experimental write-up can be regarded as the product; the demonstrated ability to respond to the open-ended extension questions is also a product. The process includes the cooperative work in obtaining the data, as well as the behavior exhibited by students as they reason and respond to the questions.

Assessing the Product: Inclusion in a Mathematics Portfolio

The experiments are well suited for inclusion in a portfolio. Completion of the Collect the Data worksheet shows that the student understands the experiment and can communicate that understanding both in writing and with a diagram. Completion of the Find the Equation worksheet demonstrates possession of basic algebra skills and knowledge of their appropriate use. Performance on the Interpret the Data worksheet provides evidence of thinking beyond mechanical manipulations.

You might ask students who have done several experiments to select one or two write-ups for inclusion in their portfolios. They should write an introduction to the selected experiment(s) to explain their choice, the mathematics they used, and the significance of the slope and intercept.

You should write a summary page, indicating for each part whether the student's work is exemplary, satisfactory, or inadequate. Include comments on the student's level of understanding.

Assessing the Process: Observation

As students work on the experiments, you can observe each group and answer these questions:

> Are both partners focused on the experiment?
>
> Is each student concentrating?
>
> Are they working independently, as well as together?
>
> What is the nature of their conversations; are they exchanging facts and discussing results?
>
> What level of understanding do the discussions showAre they observing patterns?

Note any interesting or informative student comments.

Assessing the Process: Questions

Four basic types of questions can be used to test students' understanding. One or two examples of each are given here. The Teaching Notes pages for many of the experiments suggest others. Extension questions can also be easily adapted.

Experiment-based Questions

Chris did the Bouncing Ball experiment. Here is the data he obtained.

Drop Height	Bounce Height
10	4
12	6
20	11
25	12

Use this data to find the bounce height as a function of the drop height.

Graph-based Questions

1. Julio, Chris, and Barbara all did the Ringaround experiment. Here are the graphs of their data.

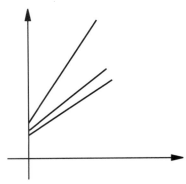

They all used marbles. Chris used large marbles, Barbara used small marbles, and Julio used medium-size marbles. Label which graph was Barbara's.

Which of these pictures most accurately shows the relative sizes of the marbles? Why?

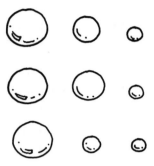

2. Dwayne and Kim both did the View Tubes experiment. Here are two points on each graph.

Dwayne	Kim
(9, 17)	(15, 27)
(23, 29)	(31, 37)

Which had the steeper graph? Why? If both their tubes were the same length, whose was fatter? Why?

Equation-based Questions

1. For the Ringaround experiment, Lee found the line $y = 2.6x + 3.5$, while Pat found the line $y = 5.3x + 2.1$. One used miniature marshmallows; the other used marbles. Can you tell which used which?

2. Tanya did the Stretching Springs II experiment. (She measured the entire length of the spring and basket.) Her equation was $y = 0.26x + 11.3$. How far did her spring stretch every time she added 4 "weights"?

Open-ended (What-if) Questions:

1. Sue and Aretha both did the Rolling Stock experiment. They used the same ramp and the same car. Sue's equation was $y = 3.6x + 5.2$, while Aretha's equation was $y = 3.1x + 20.2$. Give a possible explanation for the difference in their equations.

2. Suppose you did the Bouncing Ball experiment twice, once with a tennis ball and once with a beach ball, but forgot to label the graphs. Describe how the graphs might differ.

Teaching the Experiments

All experiments follow the same format.

Introduction—Whole Class

- Present the experiment: "If I drop this ball, how high will it bounce?"
- Demonstrate the procedure: "I'll drop it from a height of 40 inches and measure." "It bounced 28 inches."
- Identify the independent and dependent variables: "What do I decide? What's the independent variable?" "What result do I measure? What's the dependent variable?"
- Identify the experimental constants: "Will all the balls bounce the same? The results depend on which ball is dropped. We need to note that."

Write-up and Drawing—Individual Work

Before beginning the experiment, each student should complete the drawing and description of the experiment on the Collect the Data worksheet. The drawing should clearly show x and y, the independent and dependent variables. Where appropriate, equipment should be identified and measured.

Data Collection—Students Work in Pairs

Have students form cooperative learning groups of two (or three) students. Have each student in the group record the data on his or her own Collect the Data worksheet.

A test value of the independent variable should be chosen and the experiment tried. Once consistent results have been obtained, data collection should begin in earnest.

In some experiments, it is wise to repeat the measurements two or three times and take the "best" value. In some cases, this will be the middle value of y. In others, it will the maximum value or the average value. Instruct students to record only experimental data, not theoretical data, such as "if $x = 0$, then you would have . . ."

All data should be entered into the Data Collection boxes. When the collection is complete, the points to be plotted should be transferred to the Points to Be Graphed list on the right side of the page.

Graphing the Data—Students Work Individually

The students will have to choose a scale, label the axes, and plot at least five data points on the Find the Equation worksheet. The points will be approximately linear; if one point is "off," suggest that they repeat the experiment for that value of x.

Each student then looks at the points and picks the "best line" for the data that passes through two of the observed points. Partners may disagree on which points are "best."

The students then use algebra to find the equation of the line and answer the follow-up questions on the Interpret the Data worksheet. *Decimal form* means to the nearest hundredth.

Organizing and Analyzing Class Results

This whole-class activity follows the students' completion of the worksheets. Whether it is done the same day as the experiment or the following day depends on the experiment and the length of the class period.

Construct a chart of the results of each student or group (including decimal equations and graphs), noting units of measurement and relevant materials and equipment used. The chart will be used in the discussions of the follow-up questions. Reorganizing the chart, that is, sorting by units, objects, etc., will help students discover the underlining principles of the experiment.

Questions

Questions will reinforce three basic skills with the experiments. Keep in mind that many students excel in one skill, but need additional work with one of the other skills.

Experiment-based Questions

How would your graph change if you had used a longer ramp?

How would your graph change if the tube had been wider?

Graph-based Questions

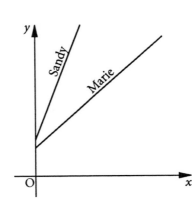

Suppose Sandy and Marie were using the same type of marbles. Why are their graphs different?

Suppose Sandy and Marie used the same glass for the experiment. Explain the difference in their graphs.

Equation-based Questions

Pat and Lee performed the Bouncing Ball experiment. Pat's equation is $y = 0.33x + 4$, while Lee's equation is $y = 0.56x + 5$. Discuss possible reasons for the differences in the equations.

Units of Measure

Selection of Units

The experiments use different systems of measurement.

Length: inches, feet, centimeters, meters

Volume: cubic centimeters, ounces, milliliters

Weight: pounds, kilograms

Non-standard units are used as well.

Length: cereal pieces, marshmallows, dried beans

Volume: cereal pieces, marbles, crackers

Weight: candies

Where it makes sense to do an experiment in either standard or metric units, separate Interpret the Data worksheets are provided. However, there are experiments for which one system is definitely preferable. In that case, the preference is stated on the first page of Teaching Notes and only one Interpret the Data worksheet is provided.

Comparison of Units

In several experiments, you are encouraged to have some groups work in standard units and other groups work in metric units. The comparison of results can be very instructive.

List the equations in decimal form, and ask whether the class can determine which groups used inches.

For similar equipment, graph a standard-unit and a metric-unit line on the same axes. Can students tell by looking which is which?

In the Circles experiment, the resulting equations are the same, no matter which units were used. Why?

Effect of Units on Slope and Intercept

On the graph: If the x-units are replaced by a larger unit, for example, centimeters by inches, the line is flatter. If the y-units are replaced by larger units, for example, seconds by minutes, the line is flatter.

In the equation: If the line is flatter, the slope is smaller.

Example: In the Bouncing Ball experiment, suppose that when the drop height is measured in inches and the bounce height is measured in inches, the line found has equation $y = 0.7x + 2$.

If the units are changed, the resulting equations are found according to the method indicated in the table.

Bounce Height	Drop Height		
	Inches	Feet	Centimeters
Inches	$y = 0.7x + 2$ $y = 8.4x + 2$	$y = (0.7 \times 12)x + 2$ $y = 0.275x + 2$	$y = (0.7/2.54)x + 2$
Feet	$y = (0.7x + 2)/12$ $y = 0.058x + 0.17$	$y = (0.7 \times 12x + 2)/12$ $y = 0.7x + 0.17$	$y = [(0.7/2.54)x + 2]/12$ $y = 0.023x + 0.17$
Centimeters	$y = (0.7x + 2) \times 2.54$ $y = 1.78x + 5.08$	$y = (0.7 \times 12x + 2) \times 2.54$ $y = 21.336x + 5.08$	$y = [(0.7/2.54)x + 2] \times 2.54$ $y = 0.7x + 5.08$

The Line of Best Fit (Linear Regression)

Every set of data has a "line of best fit." The word *best* means "better than any other"; it does not necessarily mean the line is a good fit. This line, also called the "line of linear regression," usually goes between the data points, rather than through them. The equation of this line is always given as $y = A + Bx$, where A is the intercept and B is the slope. This labeling is used by all calculators with a statistical mode. Students will need frequent reminding that the calculator finds $y = A + Bx$, not $y = Ax + B$.

When should students use a calculator to find the best line?

All students should do two or three linear experiments, using their algebraic skills to find the equation of the line through two selected data points. In later experiments, especially if partners start discussing whose line is "better," they may wish to compare their results with the regression equation $y = A + Bx$. As a rule, they will find their computed line to be close to the "best" line. (The usual reaction is for students to look at the calculator and announce that "That's right. That's what I got." The calculator has been proved right, not their own work).

At this point, you should consider the ability of the class and decide whether further algebraic practice is needed to reinforce skills. If not, by all means use a calculator to find the equation of the line of best fit.

What makes $y = A + Bx$ the "best" line?

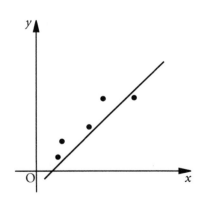

Suppose the experiment has resulted in five data points to be plotted, $(x_1, y_1), (x_2, y_2), (x_3, y_3), (x_4, y_4), (x_5, y_5)$, and that a line $y = C + Dx$ is going to be used to predict other values of y.

If the line is used, instead of the points, then $(C + Dx_1 - y_1)$ is the error in the prediction at the first point. The square of this error is $(C + Dx_1 - y_1)^2$. The sum of all the squares of the errors, called E^2, is given by the equation

$$E^2 = (C + Dx_1 - y_1)^2 + (C + Dx_2 - y_2)^2 + \ldots + (C + Dx_5 - y_5)^2.$$

The values of A and B, produced by the calculator, are the values of C and D that minimize E^2.

Remember, the best line may not be very good.

What Is r, the Correlation Coefficient?

Study these graphs. Each graphs shows five data points, the line of best fit, and the value of the correlation coefficient, *r*.

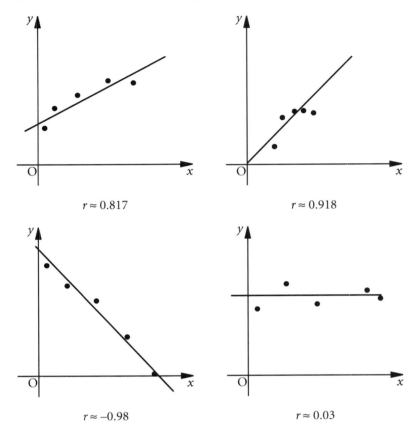

$r \approx 0.817$

$r \approx 0.918$

$r \approx -0.98$

$r \approx 0.03$

Acceptable Values for r

If $|r| > 0.98$, then the data probably represents a linear function.

If $|r| < 0.98$, then either the function was not linear, or the data is "noisy," that is, contains errors.

Remember, the purpose of *Algebra Experiments* is to investigate algebraic relationships. Students must be consistent and take reasonable care when collecting data. If this has been done, then students should decide on a line and proceed. If the *r* value is not acceptable, students should redo the experiment.

How to Find A, B, and r on a Graphing Calculator

The Texas Instruments TI-81 Graphing Calculator

Select **STAT DATA ClrStat**

Select **STAT DATA Edit**

Enter the data points, then press **(2nd) (QUIT)**

For linear regression, select **STAT LinReg**

The regression coefficients *A*, *B*, and *r* will be displayed.

The Casio fx-6300G *and* fx-7000G *Graphing Calculators*

Press (MODE) (÷)

Press (SHIFT) (AC) [the (Scl) key] (EXE)

Enter the data. To enter the point (3, 4), press ③ (SHIFT) (⎡) [the ⊙ key] ④ (DT) [the (x√⎯) key]

To see the values of *A*, *B*, and *r*, press (SHIFT) ⑦ (EXE) (SHIFT) ⑧ (EXE) (SHIFT) ⑨ (EXE)

The Casio fx-7700G *Graphing Calculator*

Press (MODE) (÷)

Press (MODE) ④

Press (MODE) (SHIFT) ① (MODE) (SHIFT) ④

Press (F2) (F3) (F1)

Enter the data. To enter the point (3, 4), press ③ (SHIFT) (⎡) [the ⊙ key] ④ (F1)

When all the data are entered, press (F6)

To see the values of *A*, *B*, and *r*, press (F1) (EXE) (F2) (EXE) (F3) (EXE)

Sample student work. Please note: student answers will vary.

Experiment 2
Ringaround

Name ___SAMPLE WORK___
Partner _____

Collect the Data

Draw a diagram of the experiment, indicating variables.

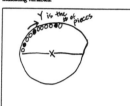

Y is the # of pieces

Describe the procedure for the experiment.

First we measured the diameter of the lid. Next we counted the number of pieces of cereal needed to make a ring around the edge of the lid.

The independent variable, x, is ___diameter___ Units ___inches___

The dependent variable, y, is ___cereal pieces___ Units ___integers___

Equipment (labels and measurements) ___Trix___

Data Collection			Points to Be Graphed	
Independent diameter	Dependent # cereal		x	y
2.7	13		2.7	13
3.3	16		3.3	16
3.7	19		3.7	19
4	20		4	20
4.4	23		4.4	23
3	14		3	14

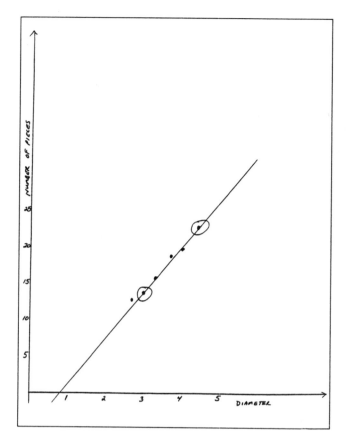

NUMBER OF PIECES (y-axis)
DIAMETER (x-axis)

Experiment 2
Ringaround

Name ___SAMPLE WORK___

Find the Equation

After plotting your data on graph paper, draw a straight line through two of your points. Choose the line that best fits your data. Circle the points on your graph and copy their coordinates below.

Your points: (3 , 14) and (4.4 , 23)

Use these points to find the equation of your line. Show your work.

Find the slope of the line.

$$m = \frac{23-14}{4.4-3} = \frac{9}{1.4} = \frac{45}{7}$$

Find the y-intercept of the line.

$$\frac{Y-14}{x-3} = \frac{45}{7}$$

$$7Y - 98 = 45x - 135$$
$$+98 \qquad +98$$

$$\frac{7Y}{7} = \frac{45x}{7} - \frac{37}{7}$$

Write the equation of the line.

$$y = \frac{45}{7}x + \frac{-37}{7}$$ rational form

$$y = 6.428x + {}^-5.285$$ decimal form

Rewrite the decimal form of the equation, using the names of the variables instead of x and y.

Cereal pieces = 6.428 · diameter + ⁻5.285

Experiment 2
Ringaround

Name ___SAMPLE WORK___

Interpret the Data

Write the decimal form of your equation here. $y = 6.428 x + {}^-5.285$

Use this equation to answer Questions 1 through 3. Show your work.

1. If the diameter were exactly 11 units, how many pieces would you need to go around the lid? ___65___

$$Y = 6.428 * 11 - 5.285$$
$$= 65.423$$

2. What would the diameter be if you needed 1001 pieces to go around the lid? ___6429___

$$Y = 6.428 * 1001 - 5.285$$
$$= 6429.13$$

3. Use your equation to find the diameter if you need 33 pieces to go around the lid. ___5.96___

$$33 = 6.428 * x - 5.285$$
$$+5.285 \qquad +5.285$$
$$\frac{38.285}{6.428} = \frac{6.428}{6.428}x$$

How does this answer compare to the answer you would get from the graph?

___It is very close.___

4. If group 6 measured the diameters in centimeters and your group used inches, whose line would be steeper? ___the group that measured in inches___

5. Label the lines in the graph, given that group 1 used unpopped popcorn and group 2 used popped popcorn.

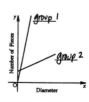

group 1
group 2
Number of Pieces
Diameter

List of the Experiments

	Experiment	Independent Variable	Dependent Variable
1	*The Wave*	number of people	time needed for wave
2	*Ringaround*	lid diameter	number of objects needed to encircle rim
3	*Shadows*	height	length of shadow
4	*Bouncing Ball*	drop height	bounce height
5	*The Raven and the Jug*	number of marbles	height of water in glass
6	*Rolling Stock*	ramp height	roll distance
7	*Stretching Springs I* Distance to Floor	number of weights	distance of basket to floor
8	*Stretching Springs II* Spring Length	number of weights	length of spring and basket
9	*Stretching Springs III* Spring Stretch	number of weights	length of spring stretch
10	*Walking the Plank*	distance from scale	weight
11	*View Tubes*	distance to object	viewable range
12	*View Tubes Extension*	diameter of tube	viewable range
13	*Candle Life*	volume of container	flame life
14	*Spilled Ink*	number of drops	diameter of water spot
15	*Sum of the Angles*	number of sides	sum of angles
16	*Circles*	circle diameter	circle circumference
17	*Cube Faces*	number of blocks in a cube	number of blocks with two exposed faces

The Wave

In this experiment, the duration of a wave is a linear function of the number of students performing it. The number of students is the *independent variable*, and the time needed to complete the wave is the *dependent variable*. This whole-class experiment provides an opportunity to model the procedures that students will use as they complete the three sections of all the experiments: Collect the Data, Find the Equation, and Interpret the Data.

Equipment

overhead projector and markers

piece of linguini (flat spaghetti)

stopwatch, or a watch that displays seconds, 1 per group

Appoint one student as the "timer."

graph paper, 1 sheet per student

rulers, 1 per student

Procedure

Start with a group of 5 students. The timer says, "Go!" and students make a wave. To do this, the first student stands up and sits down, the second student does the same, and so on. The last student says, "Stop!" as she or he sits. The timer records the elapsed time. Repeat this experiment with 8, 10, 15, and 18 students. (Continue to increase the number of students each time, until everyone in the class has been part of at least one wave.)

Plot the points on the overhead projector as students plot them at their desks. Draw a line through two of the points using a piece of spaghetti; students should use rulers. Use the graph to predict how long it would take 26 students (or some other number you didn't use) to make a wave. Have students make a 26-student wave and compare the resultant time with the prediction.

Ask: What would happen to the graph of the line if, when the timer says "Go," we all clap four times and say, "Let's go team!" before the wave begins? (The line would move up.)

Display a flatter line than the original. *Ask:* What does this graph mean? (Everyone in the class stood up and sat down faster.)

Ask: How could we change the experiment so the line would be steeper? (Each student could shout "Let's go team!")

Extension

A similar experiment can be done with dominoes. You will need a stopwatch and plenty of dominoes for this extension. Line up the dominoes about 1 inch apart. The *independent variable* is the number of dominoes, and the *dependent variable* is the amount of time it takes the dominoes to fall. Forty dominoes set 1 inch apart fall in less than 2 seconds. Varying the distance between dominoes will change the slope of the line.

The Wave

Name _____

Partner _____

Collect the Data

Draw a diagram of the experiment, indicating variables.

Describe the procedure for the experiment.

_____

_____

_____

_____

_____

_____

_____

_____

_____

The independent variable, x, is _____ Units _____

The dependent variable, y, is _____ Units _____

<table>
<tr><td colspan="2" align="center">*Data Collection*</td></tr>
<tr><td align="center">Independent</td><td align="center">Dependent</td></tr>
<tr><td>_____</td><td>_____</td></tr>
<tr><td></td><td></td></tr>
<tr><td></td><td></td></tr>
<tr><td></td><td></td></tr>
<tr><td></td><td></td></tr>
<tr><td></td><td></td></tr>
<tr><td></td><td></td></tr>
</table>

<table>
<tr><td colspan="2" align="center">*Points to Be Graphed*</td></tr>
<tr><td align="center">x</td><td align="center">y</td></tr>
<tr><td></td><td></td></tr>
<tr><td></td><td></td></tr>
<tr><td></td><td></td></tr>
<tr><td></td><td></td></tr>
<tr><td></td><td></td></tr>
<tr><td></td><td></td></tr>
</table>

Experiment 1

The Wave

Name _____

Find the Equation

After plotting your data on graph paper, draw a straight line through two of your points. Choose the line that best fits your data. Circle the points on your graph and copy their coordinates below.

Your points: (_____, _____) and (_____, _____)

Use these points to find the equation of your line. Show your work.

Find the slope of the line.

Find the *y*-intercept of the line.

Write the equation of the line.

$y =$ _____ $x +$ _____ $y =$ _____ $x +$ _____
            rational form   *decimal form*

Rewrite the decimal form of the equation, using the names of the variables instead of *x* and *y*.

_____ = _____ _____ + _____

Experiment 1

The Wave

Name _____

Interpret the Data

Write the decimal form of your equation here. $y =$ _____ $x +$ _____
Use this equation to answer Questions 1 through 5. Show your work.

1.   How long would it take 40 students to make a wave? _____

2.   How many students are needed for a 25-second wave? _____

3.   Was your answer to Question 2 a whole number? _____

      Does a non-whole number make sense for this answer? _____

4.   How many students must get up and sit down for a 3-minute wave? _____

5.   With a group of 33 students, how long would it take to make a complete wave? _____

Experiment 1

The Wave

Name _____

Interpret the Data, page 2

6. How would your graph be different if every student stood up and turned around twice before sitting down?

    _____

    _____

First- and second-hour classes did the Wave experiment. The graphs are recorded here.

7. Give a possible explanation of why the slopes are different.

    _____

    _____

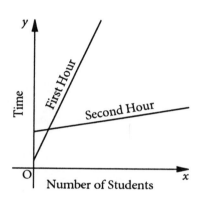

8. Give a possible explanation of why the *y*-intercepts are different.

    _____

    _____

Experiment 2
Ringaround

Teaching Notes

In this experiment, the number of objects (pieces of cereal, etc.) needed to form a ring is a linear function of the diameter of the ring. The diameter of the ring is the *independent variable,* and the number of cereal pieces is the *dependent variable.*

Equipment

assorted jar lids, 5 or 6 different sizes per group

Lids should be 3" to 8" in diameter; try lids for take-out drinks and plastic lids from coffee and peanut cans.

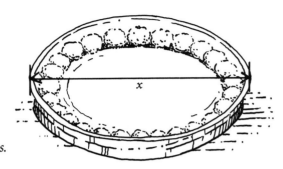

large supply of spherical-shaped breakfast cereal, dried chickpeas, or other dried beans

Pieces need not be identical. More than one type is desirable for the extension questions; label each type by letter.

rulers, 1 per group

cups or containers to hold each group's supply of cereal or beans

graph paper, 1 sheet per student

Procedure

Have groups select a circle (lid) and measure its diameter by placing a ruler across the circle. Have some groups measure in inches and others in centimeters. Diameter may be measured in inches or centimeters, but a group should use the same units throughout the experiment.

Next, have them place pieces of cereal (or beans) around the inside edge of the circle, counting as they go.

Organizing and Analyzing Class Results

Make two charts of student results, one for students that measured in centimeters and one for students that measured in inches. On each chart, record the students' graphs and decimal equations and the objects used.

For each chart, ask questions such as the following: Can you tell from the equations alone what objects were used? Can you tell from the graphs alone what objects were used?

Make the point: If you used cereal A and centimeters, your equation was approximately _____ (choose the equation of a group that used cereal A and centimeters). It doesn't matter what size of lids you used.

Ask: If we were to use regular-size marshmallows (and much larger lids) instead of cereal or beans, how might the graphs and equations change? What if someone used unpopped popcorn?

Experiment 2

Ringaround

Teaching Notes, page 2

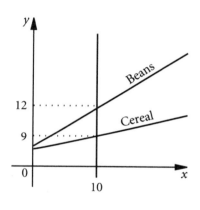

Now, sort the graphs according to the type of cereal or bean used. For those who used chickpeas, for example, *ask:* Who used centimeters? Who used inches? How can you tell from the graphs? From the equations?

Ask: If we were to use a much larger circle, like a drum from the school band, and measure the diameter in feet, how would the graph change? How would that affect the equation?

Follow the specific questions with a discussion of the meaning of the slope: Okay, you did the experiment and got your graph. What could you have done differently to get a steeper graph? (Used smaller pieces of cereal.) What else could you have done? (Measured the diameter in larger units.)

If questions arise about the *y*-intercept, ask: Is it possible to do this experiment with a circle of diameter 0? (The *y*-intercept is meaningless for this experiment.)

Extension

Have each group repeat the experiment with the same diameter measurement, but with (noticeably) different-size objects. Plot both lines on the same sheet of graph paper. Draw the vertical line $x = 10$.

Ask: What is the connection between the 9 and the 12? (Nine pieces of cereal are the same as 12 beans.) What would correspond to 36 beans? To 18 pieces of cereal? To 30 beans?

Experiment 2
Ringaround

Name _____

Partner _____

Collect the Data

Draw a diagram of the experiment, indicating variables.

Describe the procedure for the experiment.

_____

_____

_____

_____

_____

_____

_____

_____

_____

_____

The independent variable, x, is _____   Units _____

The dependent variable, y, is _____   Units _____

Equipment (labels and measurements) _____

Data Collection

Independent	Dependent

Points to Be Graphed

x	y

Experiment 2

Ringaround

Name _____

Find the Equation

After plotting your data on graph paper, draw a straight line through two of your points. Choose the line that best fits your data. Circle the points on your graph and copy their coordinates below.

Your points: (____, _____) and (____, _____)

Use these points to find the equation of your line. Show your work.

Find the slope of the line.

Find the y-intercept of the line.

Write the equation of the line.

$y =$ _____ $x +$ _____ $y =$ _____ $x +$ _____
rational form   *decimal form*

Rewrite the decimal form of the equation, using the names of the variables instead of x and y.

_____ $=$ _____ _____ $+$ _____

Experiment 2

Ringaround

Name _____

Interpret the Data

Write the decimal form of your equation here. $y =$ _____ $x +$ _____
Use this equation to answer Questions 1 through 3. Show your work.

1. If the diameter were exactly 11 units, how many pieces would you need to
    go around the lid? _____

2. What would the diameter be if you needed 1001 pieces to go around
    the lid? _____

3. Use your equation to find the diameter if you need 33 pieces to go around
    the lid. _____

    How does this answer compare to the answer you would get from the
    graph?

    _____

    _____

4. If group 6 measured the diameters in centimeters and your group used
    inches, whose line would be steeper? _____

5. Label the lines in the graph, given that group 1 used unpopped popcorn
    and group 2 used popped popcorn.

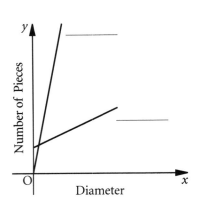

Experiment 3
Shadows

Teaching Notes

In this experiment, the length of the shadow is a linear function of the height of the object casting the shadow. Each group of two students will select objects to measure. The height of the object is the *independent variable*, and the length of the object's shadow is the *dependent variable*.

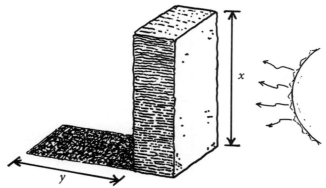

Equipment

    rulers, tape measures, or yardsticks, 1 per group

    objects tall enough to be measured and to make a shadow

    graph paper, 1 sheet per student

Procedure

This experiment requires daylight. Best results are obtained if you do not do this experiment around noon and if you use thin objects, at least 10 inches tall. Be flexible in your plans if it is not a sunny day.

If there are at least 12 groups, have half the groups measure in centimeters, the other half in inches. Keep the data separate; at the end of the experiment you may want to compare the equations and graphs.

Experiment 3

Shadows

Name _____

Partner _____

Collect the Data

Draw a diagram of the experiment, indicating variables.

Describe the procedure for the experiment.

_____

_____

_____

_____

_____

_____

_____

_____

_____

The independent variable, *x*, is _____   Units _____

The dependent variable, *y*, is _____   Units _____

Equipment (Labels and measurements) _____

_____

Data Collection

Independent	Dependent

Points to Be Graphed

x	*y*

Experiment 3

Shadows

Name _____

Find the Equation

After plotting your data on graph paper, draw a straight line through two of your points. Choose the line that best fits your data. Circle the points on your graph and copy their coordinates below.

Your points: (____, _____) and (____, _____)

Use these points to find the equation of your line. Show your work.

Find the slope of the line.

Find the *y*-intercept of the line.

Write the equation of the line.

$y =$ _____ $x +$ _____ $y =$ _____ $x +$ _____
                  rational form   *decimal form*

Rewrite the decimal form of the equation, using the names of the variables instead of *x* and *y*.

_____ = _____ _____ + _____

Experiment 3

Shadows

Name _____

Interpret the Data
Metric Measures

Write the decimal form of your equation here. $y =$ _____ $x +$ _____

Use this equation to answer Questions 1 through 3. Show your work.

1.   If the object you used were 91 cm high, what would be the length of the
     shadow? _____

2.   Find the height of an object that would make a shadow 43 cm in length.
     _____

3.   Find the height of an object that would make a shadow 61 cm in length.
     _____

4.   Explain how your line would be different if you did the experiment at noon.

     _____

     _____

     _____

5.   At what time of day do you think the slope of your line would be
     the steepest? _____ The flattest? _____

6.   Your classmate Juanita makes her measurements in inches. If she does her
     experiment at the same time you do yours, will her line have the same
     slope as yours? _____ Will it be parallel, or will it intersect?
     _____

7.   If your school has a flagpole, measure its shadow and determine its height. _____
     Check with the building maintenance staff to determine the accuracy of your answer.

30

Experiment 3

Shadows

Name _____

Interpret the Data
Standard Measures

Write the decimal form of your equation here. $y =$ _____ $x +$ _____
Use this equation to answer Questions 1 through 3. Show your work.

1. If the object you used were 42 inches high, what would be the length of the
    shadow? _____

2. Find the height of an object that would make a shadow 18 inches in length.
    _____

3. Find the height of an object that would make a shadow 25 inches in length.
    _____

4. Explain how your line would be different if you did the experiment at noon.

    _____

    _____

    _____

5. At what time of day do you think the slope of your line would be
    the steepest? _____ The flattest? _____

6. Your classmate Juanita makes her measurements in centimeters. If she
    does her experiment at the same time you do yours, will her line have the
    same slope as yours? _____ Will it be parallel, or will it intersect?
    _____

7. If your school has a flagpole, measure its shadow and determine its height. _____
    Check with the building maintenance staff to determine the accuracy of your answer.

Experiment 4
Bouncing Ball

Teaching Notes

In this experiment, the height of the bounce is a linear function of the height of the drop. The drop height of a ball is the *independent variable,* and the height of the ball's bounce is the *dependent variable.* This experiment doesn't need much introduction, but measuring the height of the bounce takes practice.

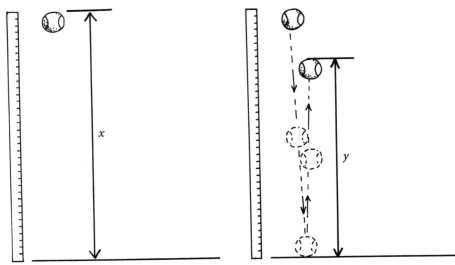

Equipment

assorted balls (tennis balls, golf balls, table tennis balls, racquet balls, super balls), 1 per group

Number the balls. Use at least two of each type.

yardsticks or metersticks, 1 per group

graph paper, 1 sheet per student

Procedure

Students work in groups of two. The first student drops a ball from a given height (the drop height); the second students measures the distance from the top of the ball to the ground (the bounce height).

Have partners practice taking measurements until they are getting consistent results. If, when their points are plotted, the group finds that one point is badly out of line, they should redo that drop height. Students may use either inches or centimeters.

For each value of the independent variable, students should drop the ball three times and select their "best" (most accurate) measurement of the bounce height as the y-value to be graphed.

Organizing and Analyzing Class Results

List only the decimal forms of the equations. Ask students to identify which lines represent tennis balls, golf balls, and so on. Discuss the meaning of slopes and intercepts. (Slope indicates "bounciness"; intercept is theoretically the ball's diameter.) A negative intercept is likely. Ask students for possible explanations.

Experiment 4
Bouncing Ball

Name _____

Partner _____

Collect the Data

Draw a diagram of the experiment, indicating variables.

[ ]

Describe the procedure for the experiment.

_____

_____

_____

_____

_____

_____

_____

_____

_____

_____

The independent variable, x, is _____ Units _____

The dependent variable, y, is _____ Units _____

Equipment (labels and measurements)

Type of ball _____ Number _____ Diameter _____

Data Collection

Independent _____	Dependent _____		
	Trial 1	Trial 2	Trial 3

Points to Be Graphed

x	y

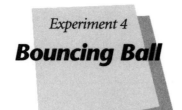

Bouncing Ball

Name _____

Find the Equation

After plotting your data on graph paper, draw a straight line through two of
your points. Choose the line that best fits your data. Circle the points on your
graph and copy their coordinates below.

Your points: (____, _____) and (____, _____)

Use these points to find the equation of your line. Show your work.

Find the slope of the line.

Find the *y*-intercept of the line.

Write the equation of the line.

$$y = \underline{\hspace{2cm}} x + \underline{\hspace{2cm}} \qquad\qquad y = \underline{\hspace{2cm}} x + \underline{\hspace{2cm}}$$
$$\text{\textit{rational form}} \qquad\qquad\qquad \text{\textit{decimal form}}$$

Rewrite the decimal form of the equation, using the names of the variables instead of *x* and *y*.

_____ = _____ _____ + _____

Experiment 4

Bouncing Ball

Name_____

Interpret the Data
Metric Measures

Write the decimal form of your equation here. $y =$ _____ $x +$ _____
Use this equation to answer Questions 1 through 3. Show your work.

1.   If you were to drop the ball from a height of 210 cm, how high would it bounce? _____

2.   If your ball bounces 123 cm, what was the drop height? _____

3.   If the height of your ball's bounce is 72 cm, what was the drop height? _____

4.   How would your graph be different if you'd used a "super ball"? (If you used a super ball in your experiment, answer the question for a tennis ball.)

     _____

     _____

     _____

5.   Julio's slope was $\frac{13}{19}$ and Chris's slope was $\frac{14}{29}$. Who used the tennis ball and who used the golf ball? How do you know?

     _____

     _____

     _____

6.   If you were to drop the ball from a height of 210 cm, how high would the second bounce be? _____

     Find a place where you can test your answer.

Experiment 4

Bouncing Ball

Name_____

Interpret the Data
Standard Measures

Write the decimal form of your equation here. $y = $ _____ $x + $ _____
Use this equation to answer Questions 1 through 3. Show your work.

1. If you were to drop the ball from a height of 90 inches, how high would it bounce? _____

2. If your ball bounces 55 inches, what was the drop height? _____

3. If the height of your ball's bounce is 34 inches, what was the drop height? _____

4. How would your graph be different if you had used a "super ball"? (If you used a super ball in your experiment, answer the question for a tennis ball.)

    _____

    _____

    _____

5. Julio's slope was $\frac{13}{19}$ and Chris's slope was $\frac{14}{29}$. Who used the tennis ball and who used the golf ball? How do you know?

    _____

    _____

    _____

6. If you were to drop the ball you used from a height of 90 inches, how high would the second bounce be? _____

    Test the accuracy of your answer.

The Raven and the Jug

Teaching Notes

In this experiment, the depth of the water in the glass is a linear function of the number of marbles that have been added. The *independent variable* is the number of marbles that have been added to the water, and the *dependent variable* is the depth of the water.

Equipment

marbles, uniform in size, 60 per group

> *In a standard bag of marbles, there is much variation in size. Students should try to use uniform-size marbles. For best results, different types of marbles, such as clear, black, and swirly, should not be mixed.*

straight-sided, flat-bottomed 8–10 oz. drinking glasses, or soup cans, 1 per group

centimeter rulers, 1 per group

water

> *If soup cans are used, color the water.*

graph paper, 1 sheet per student

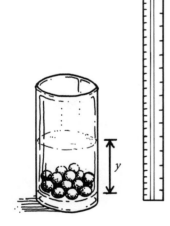

Procedure

Fill the glass one-third to one-half full of water, until a convenient level is reached; 5.5 cm to 6 cm is usually satisfactory. Add marbles, at least 5 at a time, and record the water level. The marbles must remain submerged.

Although the independent variable is the number of marbles added, you may find students adding marbles until the level rises a half centimeter.

The data will be emphatically linear. The slope has a clear physical meaning: If every time 8 marbles are added, the level increases by $\frac{1}{2}$ cm, the slope will be

$$\frac{\frac{1}{2}}{8}.$$

The *y*-intercept is the water level before any marbles have been added.

Extension

Here are three ways of asking the same questions:

Experiment-based

How would the line change if you had used larger marbles?

How would your line change if the glass had been narrower?

Graph-based

Draw this graph on the board.

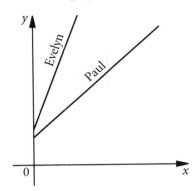

Say: Suppose Evelyn and Paul used the same type of marbles. Why are their graphs different?

Suppose Evelyn and Paul had used the same glass for the experiment. Explain the difference in their graphs.

Equation-based

Pat's equation is $y = 0.33x + 4$

Lee's equation is $y = 0.56x + 5$

Discuss possible descriptions of their experiments.

Slope representations

Questions 4, 5, and 6 can lead to discovery of the physical significance of different representations of the slope. Suppose students discover from Questions 4 and 5 that 17 marbles are needed to raise the water level 1 cm. The slope of their line will be approximately $\frac{1}{17}$. If the slope were approximately $\frac{1}{17}$, then the answer to Question 6 is the solution to $\frac{z}{17} = \frac{1}{17}$, or $z = \frac{10}{17}$.

Experiment 5

The Raven and the Jug

Name _____

Partner _____

Collect the Data

Draw a diagram of the experiment, indicating variables.

Describe the procedure for the experiment.

_____

_____

_____

_____

_____

_____

_____

_____

_____

_____

The independent variable, *x*, is _____   Units _____

The dependent variable, *y*, is _____   Units _____

Equipment (labels and measurements) _____

_____

Data Collection

Independent	Dependent
_____	_____

Points to Be Graphed

x	*y*

Experiment 5

The Raven and the Jug

Name _____

Find the Equation

After plotting your data on graph paper, draw a straight line through two of your points. Choose the line that best fits your data. Circle the points on your graph and copy their coordinates below.

Your points: (____, _____) and (____, _____)

Use these points to find the equation of your line. Show your work.

Find the slope of the line.

Find the *y*-intercept of the line.

Write the equation of the line.

$y =$ _____ $x +$ _____ $y =$ _____ $x +$ _____

          rational form   *decimal form*

Rewrite the decimal form of the equation, using the names of the variables instead of *x* and *y*.

_____ $=$ _____ _____ $+$ _____

Experiment 5

The Raven and the Jug

Name _____

Interpret the Data

Write the decimal form of your equation here. $y =$ _____ $x +$ _____
Use this equation to answer the questions. Show your work.

1.   How high would the water level be if 31 marbles were submerged? _____

2.   How many marbles are needed to make the water level exactly 6.75 cm? _____

3.   How many marbles are needed to make the water level exactly 8.75 cm? _____

4.   How many marbles are needed to make the water rise 4.5 cm? _____

5.   How many marbles are needed to make the water rise 5.5 cm? _____

6.   How much does the water rise for every 10 marbles you add? _____

Experiment 6

Rolling Stock

Teaching Notes

In this experiment, the distance a car rolls from the end of the ramp is a linear function of the height of the ramp. The ramp height is the *independent variable*, and the distance the car rolls from the end of the ramp is the *dependent variable*.

Equipment

marbles or small toy cars, 1 per group

If the floor is bare, use toy cars. Number them and be sure they roll freely. If the room is carpeted, use marbles.

ramps of varying lengths, 15"–22"

Number the ramps. If they are made from slats of wood, bevel the downhill end. Vinyl gutters are inexpensive; most building-supply stores will cut up a 10-foot length for you.

blocks, books, or another material to raise the ramps

yardsticks, 1 per group

graph paper, 1 sheet per student

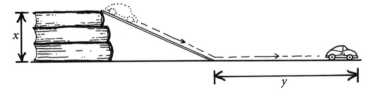

Procedure

In this experiment, the independent variable is the vertical distance and the dependent variable is a horizontal distance; this should not be the first experiment students conduct. The problems caused by the labels *x* and *y* are minimized if students are already accustomed to putting the coordinates of the points to be plotted in columns.

The "best" measurement in this experiment will be the farthest the car traveled for the given ramp height. If you are using marbles, the "best" measurement in this experiment will be the average or middle distance for the given ramp height.

Students will find an equation in the form $y = mx + b$, where $x = h$, the height, and $y = d$, the distance. Emphasize to them that the equation means:

$$\text{Roll distance} = m \times \text{Ramp height} + b.$$

That is, roll distance is a linear function of ramp height.

Have students start the car's rear wheels at the high end of the ramp. Because cars may swerve or lose distance due to friction or bounce, the measurements will tend to be small. Rather than taking an average, use the largest value of the dependent variable. Ramp height should be high enough to move the car, but not so steep as to cause the car to crash. A 15-inch ramp should not be raised more than 8 inches.

For a given ramp height, the *independent variable*, have students measure the distance the car rolls from the end of the ramp, the *dependent variable*.

Because of the relative magnitudes of *x* and *y*, students will have to use different scales while graphing their points. The chosen scale will affect the apparent slope of the graph, but not the equation.

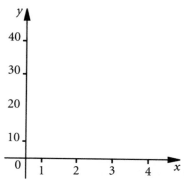

Extension

Say: Suppose you measure the total distance the car travels (including the ramp). How would your graph be different?

Instead of having students measure the distance the car traveled as the dependent variable, have them measure the distance from where the car stops to a fixed object such as the wall on the other side of the room. They will get a negative slope and a non-zero *y*-intercept.

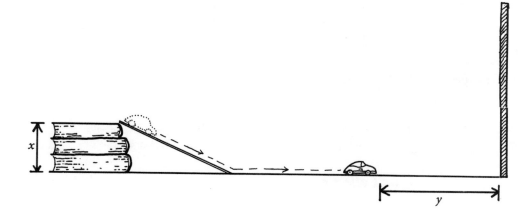

Experiment 6

Rolling Stock

Name _____

Partner _____

Collect the Data

Draw a diagram of the experiment, indicating variables.

Describe the procedure for the experiment.

The independent variable, *x*, is _____ Units _____

The dependent variable, *y*, is _____ Units _____

Equipment (labels and measurements)   Ramp number _____   Length _____

Car _____   Car number _____   or Marble diameter _____

Data Collection

Independent _____	Dependent _____		
	Trial 1	Trial 2	Trial 3

Points to Be Graphed

x	y

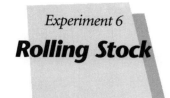

Experiment 6

Rolling Stock

Name _____

Find the Equation

After plotting your data on graph paper, draw a straight line through two of
your points. Choose the line that best fits your data. Circle the points on your
graph and copy their coordinates below.

Your points: (_____, _____) and (_____, _____)

Use these points to find the equation of your line. Show your work.

Find the slope of the line.

Find the *y*-intercept of the line.

Write the equation of the line.

$y =$ _____ $x +$ _____ $y =$ _____ $x +$ _____
                rational form   *decimal form*

Rewrite the decimal form of the equation, using the names of the variables instead of *x* and *y*.

_____ = _____ _____ + _____

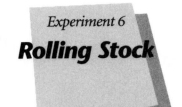

Experiment 6

Rolling Stock

Name _____

Interpret the Data
Metric Measures

Write the decimal form of your equation here. $y =$ _____ $x +$ _____
Use this equation to answer Questions 1 through 3. Show your work.

1. How far would the car (or marble) roll if the height of the ramp were
    13 cm? _____

2. How high would the ramp need to be to have the car (or marble) roll
    exactly 51 cm? _____

3. How high would the ramp need to be to have the car (or marble) roll
    exactly 122 cm? _____

4. Jerry and Arnetta used identical marbles and the same length ramp. Jerry
    worked in the carpeted library and Arnetta was in the tiled cafeteria. Label
    their graphs.

5. Describe what you expect would happen to your original graph if the floor
    were carpeted.

    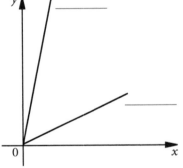

    _____

    _____

6. Describe what you expect would happen to your original graph if you used
    a longer ramp.

    _____

    _____

7. If a longer ramp is available, use your same car (or marble) to test your
    expectations. What happened?

    _____

    _____

8. How high can you raise your ramp and still have the car (or marble) roll
    without crashing? _____

Name _____

Interpret the Data
Standard Measures

Write the decimal form of your equation here. $y = $ _____ $x + $ _____

Use this equation to answer Questions 1 through 3. Show your work.

1.   How far would the car (or marble) roll if the height of the ramp were
       4.2 inches? _____

2.   How high would the ramp need to be to have the car (or marble) roll
       exactly 22 inches? _____

3.   How high would the ramp need to be to have the car (or marble) roll
       exactly 52 inches? _____

4.   Jerry and Arnetta used identical marbles and the same length ramp. Jerry
       worked in the carpeted library and Arnetta was in the tiled cafeteria. Label
       their graphs.

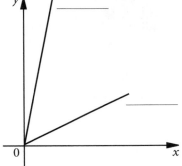

5.   Describe what you expect would happen to your original graph if the floor
       were carpeted.

       _____

       _____

6.   Describe what you expect would happen to your original graph if you used
       a longer ramp.

       _____

       _____

7.   If a longer ramp is available, use your same car (or marble) to test your
       expectations. What happened?

       _____

       _____

8.   How high can you raise your ramp and still have the car (or marble) roll
       without crashing? _____

Experiment 7

Stretching Springs I

Distance to Floor

Teaching Notes

In this experiment, the distance from the bottom of the basket to the floor is a linear function of the number of weights in the basket. The number of weights in the basket is the *independent variable,* and the distance from the bottom of the basket to the floor is the *dependent variable.* The three Stretching Springs experiments will allow students to explore positive and negative slopes as well as the meaning of the *y*-intercept.

Equipment

springs, 1 per group

Number the springs. Small metal Slinkies™ cut in half are appealing. Bend one end to form a hook.

tape

paper clips

film, cream, or paper ketchup containers, 1 per group

sets of uniform "weights"

Use candy-coated chocolates, X-shaped paper clips, or any other small candy. Put in "baskets" made from the paper clips and film, cream, or paper ketchup containers. A film container holds approximately 20 pieces of candy. Form the handle as shown so the basket doesn't tip. Paper clips can hang directly from the spring without baskets. If paper clips are used, the dependent variable is the distance from the floor to the bottom of the spring.

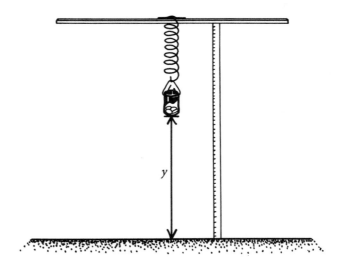

yardsticks, 2 per group

Metersticks are generally too thick for this experiment.

graph paper, 1 sheet per student

Stretching Springs I

Distance to Floor

Teaching Notes, page 2

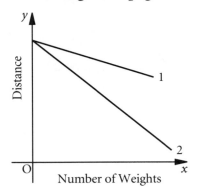

Procedure

Have students place a yardstick across two desks or chairs and hang the spring and empty basket. One yardstick is for measurement and one is for suspending the spring. Have them use tape to secure the spring to the yardstick. Then have students add 3 or 4 weights at a time.

Extension

Draw the following graph on the board.

Explain: Shawn did the Stretching Springs I experiment using one type of weight, and Maria did the experiment using a lighter weight. Which is Maria's graph?

Stretching Springs I

Distance to Floor

Name _____

Partner _____

Collect the Data

Draw a diagram of the experiment, indicating variables.

Describe the procedure for the experiment.

_____

_____

_____

_____

_____

_____

_____

_____

_____

_____

The independent variable, x, is _____   Units _____

The dependent variable, y, is _____   Units _____

Equipment (labels and measurements)   Spring number _____   Type of weight _____

Data Collection	
Independent	Dependent

Points to Be Graphed	
x	y

**Stretching Springs
I**

Distance to Floor

Name _____

Find the Equation

After plotting your data on graph paper, draw a straight line through two of
your points. Choose the line that best fits your data. Circle the points on your
graph and copy their coordinates below.

Your points: (_____, _____) and (_____, _____)

Use these points to find the equation of your line. Show your work.

Find the slope of the line.

Find the *y*-intercept of the line.

Write the equation of the line.

$$y = \underline{\hspace{2cm}} x + \underline{\hspace{2cm}}$$
rational form

$$y = \underline{\hspace{2cm}} x + \underline{\hspace{2cm}}$$
decimal form

Rewrite the decimal form of the equation, using the names of the variables instead of *x* and *y*.

_____ = _____ _____ + _____

Stretching Springs
I
Distance to Floor

Name _____

Interpret the Data
Metric Measures

Write the decimal form of your equation here. $y =$ _____ $x +$ _____
Use this equation to answer the questions. Show your work.

1.   How far would the basket be from the floor if 11 weights were used? _____

2.   How many weights were used if the basket is 34 cm from the floor? _____

3.   How many weights were used if the basket is 20 cm from the floor? _____

4.   What is the meaning of the *y*-intercept of your graph?

   _____

   _____

   _____

5.   How much is the spring stretched by 9 weights? _____

Experiment 7

Stretching Springs
I
Distance to Floor

Name _____

Interpret the Data
Standard Measures

Write the decimal form of your equation here. $y = $ _____ $x + $ _____
Use this equation to answer the questions. Show your work.

1.   How far would the basket be from the floor if 11 weights were used? _____

2.   How many weights were used if the basket is 14 inches from the floor? _____

3.   How many weights were used if the basket is 6 inches from the floor? _____

4.   What is the meaning of the *y*-intercept of your graph?

     _____

     _____

     _____

5.   How much is the spring stretched by 9 weights? _____

Experiment 8
Stretching Springs II
Spring Length

Teaching Notes

In this experiment, the total length of the spring and basket is a linear function of the number of weights. The number of weights in the basket is the *independent variable*, and the length of the spring and basket is the *dependent variable*. The three Stretching Springs experiments will allow students to explore positive and negative slopes as well as the meaning of the *y*-intercept.

Equipment

springs, 1 per group

> *Number the springs. Small metal Slinkies™ cut in half are appealing. Bend one end to form a hook.*

tape

paper clips

film, cream, or paper ketchup containers, 1 per group

sets of uniform "weights"

> *Use candy-coated chocolates, X-shaped paper clips, or any other small candy. Put in "baskets" made from the paper clips and film, cream, or paper ketchup containers. A film container holds approximately 20 pieces of candy. Form the handle as shown so the basket doesn't tip. Paper clips can hang directly from the spring without baskets. If paper clips are used, the dependent variable is the distance from the ruler to the bottom of the spring.*

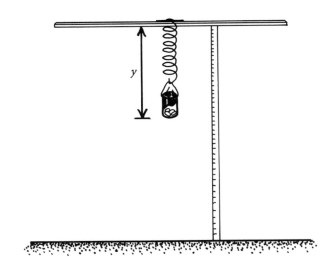

yardsticks, 2 per group

> *Metersticks are generally too thick for this experiment.*

graph paper, 1 sheet per student

Stretching Springs II

Spring Length

Teaching Notes, page 2

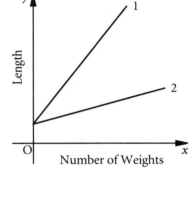

Procedure

Have groups place a yardstick across two desks or chairs and hang the spring and basket without weights. One yardstick is for measurement and one is for suspending the spring. Have them use tape to secure the spring to the yardstick.

Now, groups add three or four weights.

Extension

Draw the following graph on the board.

Explain: Kris did the Stretching Springs II experiment using one size of candy, and Coretta did the experiment using a small size of candy. Which is Coretta's graph?

After doing Stretching Springs experiments I and II, have the class graph both lines on the same sheet of graph paper. The *y*-coordinates will always add to the distance from the yardstick to the floor.

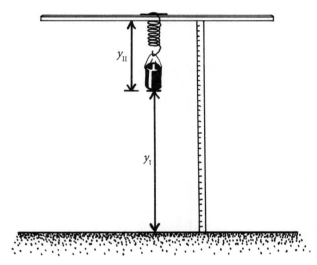

If, for example

$$y_I = -0.3x + 27$$

and

$$y_I + y_{II} = 40$$

(the distance from the top of the spring to the floor), then

$$40 - y_{II} = -0.3x + 27$$

or

$$y_{II} = 0.3x + 13.$$

The lines are not pependicular.

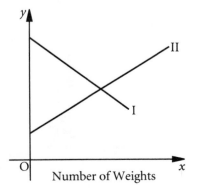

Experiment 8
Stretching Springs II
Spring Length

Name _____

Partner _____

Collect the Data

Draw a diagram of the experiment, indicating variables.

Describe the procedure for the experiment.

_____

_____

_____

_____

_____

_____

_____

_____

_____

_____

The independent variable, x, is _____   Units _____

The dependent variable, y, is _____   Units _____

Equipment (labels and measurements)   Spring number _____   Type of weight _____

Data Collection

Independent	Dependent

Points to Be Graphed

x	y

Stretching Springs II

Spring Length

Name _____

Find the Equation

After plotting your data on graph paper, draw a straight line through two of your points. Choose the line that best fits your data. Circle the points on your graph and copy their coordinates below.

Your points: (_____, _____) and (_____, _____)

Use these points to find the equation of your line. Show your work.

Find the slope of the line.

Find the *y*-intercept of the line.

Write the equation of the line.

$y =$ _____ $x +$ _____ $y =$ _____ $x +$ _____
              rational form   *decimal form*

Rewrite the decimal form of the equation, using the names of the variables instead of *x* and *y*.

_____ = _____ _____ + _____

Experiment 8

Stretching Springs II

Spring Length

Name _____

Interpret the Data
Metric Measures

Write the decimal form of your equation here. $y =$ _____ $x +$ _____
Use this equation to answer the questions. Show your work.

1.   How long would the spring be if 11 weights were used? _____

2.   If the total length of the spring and basket is 36 cm, how many weights are
      in the basket? _____

3.   If the total length of the spring and basket is 67 cm, how many weights are
      in the basket? _____

4.   What is the meaning of the *y*-intercept of your graph?

      _____

5.   Use the slope of your line to determine how much the spring stretches
      every time 7 weights are added. _____

6.   Describe what you expect would happen to the original graph if you were
      to use heavier weights.

      _____

      _____

Experiment 8
Stretching Springs II
Spring Length

Name _____

Interpret the Data
Standard Measures

Write the decimal form of your equation here. $y =$ _____ $x +$ _____
Use this equation to answer the questions. Show your work.

1.   How long would the spring be if 11 weights were used? _____

2.   If the total length of the spring and basket is 16 inches, how many weights
     are in the basket? _____

3.   If the total length of the spring and basket is 25 inches, how many weights
     are in the basket? _____

4.   What is the meaning of the y-intercept of your graph?

     _____

5.   Use the slope of your line to determine how much the spring stretches
     every time 7 weights are added. _____

6.   Describe what you expect would happen to the original graph if you were
     to use heavier weights.

     _____

     _____

Stretching Springs III

Spring Stretch

Teaching Notes

In this experiment, the stretch of the spring is a linear function of the number of weights. The number of weights in the basket is the *independent variable*, and the stretch of the spring is the *dependent variable*. The three Stretching Springs experiments will allow students to explore positive and negative slopes as well as the meaning of the *y*-intercept.

Equipment

springs, 1 per group

> *Number the springs. Small metal Slinkies™ cut in half are appealing. Bend one end to form a hook.*

tape

paper clips

film, cream, or paper ketchup containers, 1 per group

sets of uniform "weights"

> *Use candy-coated chocolates, X-shaped paper clips, or any other small candy. Put in "baskets" made from the paper clips and film, cream, or paper ketchup containers. A film container holds approximately 20 pieces of candy. Form the handle as shown so the basket doesn't tip. Paper clips can hang directly from the spring without baskets.*

yardsticks, 2 per group

> *Metersticks are generally too thick for this experiment.*

graph paper, 1 sheet per student

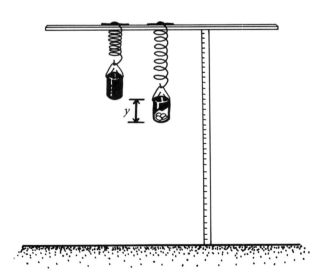

Procedure

Have students place a yardstick across two desks or chairs and hang the spring and basket without weights. One yardstick is for measurement and one is for suspending the spring. Have them use tape to secure the spring to the yardstick.

Have students make a note of the original length. Then, they add a number of weights as the *independent variable*, and measure the amount of stretch from the spring's original length as the *dependent variable*.

If students have done Stretching Springs experiments I or II, they can generate the data for Stretching Springs III by subtraction.

Extension

Draw the following graph on the board.

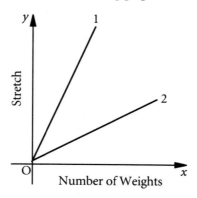

Explain: Carlos did the Stretching Springs III experiment using one size of candy, and Sandy did the experiment using a smaller size of candy. Which is Sandy's graph?

Experiment 9
Stretching Springs III
Spring Stretch

Name _____

Partner _____

Collect the Data

Draw a diagram of the experiment, indicating variables.

Describe the procedure for the experiment.

_____

_____

_____

_____

_____

_____

_____

_____

_____

_____

The independent variable, x, is _____ Units _____

The dependent variable, y, is _____ Units _____

Equipment (labels and measurements)   Spring number _____   Type of weight _____

Data Collection
Independent	Dependent
_____	_____

Points to Be Graphed
x	y

62

Stretching Springs III

Spring Stretch

Name _____

Find the Equation

After plotting your data on graph paper, draw a straight line through two of your points. Choose the line that best fits your data. Circle the points on your graph and copy their coordinates below.

Your points: (____, _____) and (____, _____)

Use these points to find the equation of your line. Show your work.

Find the slope of the line.

Find the *y*-intercept of the line.

Write the equation of the line.

$y =$ _____ $x +$ _____ $y =$ _____ $x +$ _____
        rational form   *decimal form*

Rewrite the decimal form of the equation, using the names of the variables instead of *x* and *y*.

_____ = _____ _____ + _____

Experiment 9
Stretching Springs III
Spring Stretch

Name _____

Interpret the Data
Metric Measures

Write the decimal form of your equation here. $y =$ _____ $x +$ _____
Use this equation to answer the questions. Show your work.

1. How much would the spring stretch if 11 weights were in the basket?

    _____

2. If your spring has stretched 22 cm, how many weights did you use?

    _____

3. If your spring has stretched 31 cm, how many weights are in the basket?

    _____

4. What will be the total length of the spring stretched by 11 weights?

    _____

5. Ana did all three Stretching Springs experiments. Label the dependent variable for each graph.

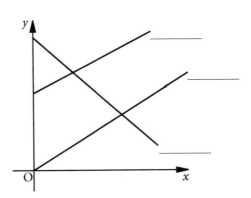

Experiment 9
Stretching Springs
III
Spring Stretch

Name _____

Interpret the Data
Standard Measures

Write the decimal form of your equation here. $y =$ _____ $x +$ _____
Use this equation to answer the questions. Show your work.

1. How much would the spring stretch if 11 weights were in the basket?

   _____

2. If your spring has stretched 8 inches, how many weights did you use?

   _____

3. If your spring has stretched 13 inches, how many weights are in the basket?

   _____

4. What will be the total length of the spring stretched by 11 weights?

   _____

5. Ana did all three Stretching Springs experiments. Label the dependent variable for each graph.

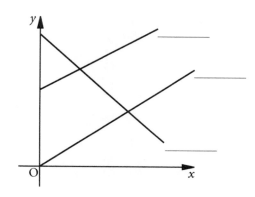

Walking the Plank

Teaching Notes

In this experiment, the weight of a student is a linear function of the distance of the student from the scale. The distance to the scale end of the plank is the *independent variable*, and the weight of student is the *dependent variable*. This experiment produces a line with a negative slope, and both the x- and y-intercept have physical significance.

Equipment

bathroom scale, 1 per group

Number the scales.

plank or board, 2" thick by 6" wide and at least 7' long, 1 per group

Number the planks.

yardstick or tape measure, 1 per group

graph paper, 1 sheet per student

Procedure

Have groups put one end of the plank on the scale (in the middle of the scale). Support the other end of the plank with a brick or a block of wood about the same height as the scale. Explain that one student will stand on the plank, and the other will measure the distance to the scale end of the plank and record the weight. Remind the groups that the same student must walk the plank for the entire experiment.

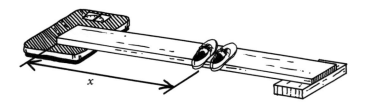

Make sure students are consistent when measuring the distance from their feet to the scale end of the plank (for example, always measure from the left foot).

Experiment 10

Walking the Plank

Name _____

Partner _____

Collect the Data

Draw a diagram of the experiment, indicating variables

Describe the procedure for the experiment.

The independent variable, x, is _____   Units _____

The dependent variable, y, is _____   Units _____

Equipment (labels and measurements)   Scale number _____
Plank number _____   Length _____

Data Collection		Second set of data (Question 6)	Points to Be Graphed		(Second set)	
Independent	Dependent		x	y	x	y

Experiment 10

Walking the Plank

Find the Equation

Name _____

After plotting your data on graph paper, draw a straight line through two of your points. Choose the line that best fits your data. Circle the points on your graph and copy their coordinates below.

Your points: (____, _____) and (____, _____)

Use these points to find the equation of your line. Show your work.

Find the slope of the line.

Find the *y*-intercept of the line.

Write the equation of the line.

$y =$ _____ $x +$ _____ $y =$ _____ $x +$ _____
        rational form   *decimal form*

Rewrite the decimal form of the equation, using the names of the variables instead of *x* and *y*.

_____ = _____ _____ + _____

Experiment 10

Walking the Plank

Name _____

Interpret the Data

Write the decimal form of your equation here. $y =$ _____ $x +$ _____
Use this equation to answer the questions. Show your work.

1.   What weight will be recorded if the person is 5.25 feet away from the scale?
     _____

2.   If the scale shows a weight of 75 pounds, how far away is the student from
     the scale end of the plank? _____

3.   If the scale shows a weight of 52 pounds, how far away is the student from
     the scale end of the plank? _____

4.   As the student moves farther and farther from the scale, what happens to
     the reading?

     _____

     _____

5.   Study the graph to the right.

     Determine the weight of the person walking the plank. _____

     Determine the length of the plank. _____

6.   Change roles with your partner and collect another set of data. Plot the
     second set of points on your graph paper and draw a line. What do the
     lines have in common? _____

     Why? _____

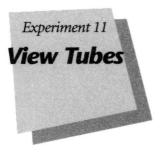

Experiment 11
View Tubes

Teaching Notes

In this experiment, the viewable vertical distance is a linear function of the distance from the wall. The distance from the wall is the *independent variable*, and the viewable vertical distance is the *dependent variable*. In Experiment 12, View Tubes Extension, the independent variable is changed to the diameter of the tube.

Equipment

assorted tubes, 1 per group

> *Number the tubes. Try to have several tubes of the same length but different diameters, and some of the same diameter but different lengths. Tubes from kitchen wraps (plastic, wax paper, foil) work well. Sawed-off lengths from the core of a carpet or fabric bolt add variety. Cut them long enough so that rolling the eye doesn't distort the measurements.*

yardsticks, 2 per group

graph paper, 1 sheet per student

Procedure

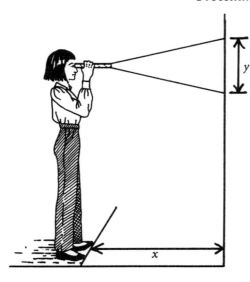

Students work in groups of two or three. Students wearing glasses should not be paired with students who do not.

All students should record their viewable vertical distance for each value of x and average the measured values for plotting.

Reasonable accuracy is obtained if students measure the distance from the toes. In theory, the intercept is the diameter of the tube; rough measurement may lead to a straight line with a negative intercept.

Students will have to decide on units. (Measuring the distance from the wall in feet and the viewable vertical distance in inches works well. Some students, however, will not want to use different units for the two variables.)

Have students obtain all their points first, then decide how to scale their graphs. If their x-measurements are 4, 5, 6, and 7 (that is, close together), they should allow 5 squares to a unit on the graph.

Organizing and Analyzing Class Results

Collect the students' results. Record length and diameter of tube as well as the equation. Post several graphs. Investigate the relationship between the dimensions of the tubes and the slopes and intercepts. Then, ask the class to identify which tube produced each graph.

Post several slopes and ask which of the tubes might have been used for each equation.

See Experiment 12 for a mathematical explanation of the function.

Experiment 11
View Tubes

Name _____

Partner _____

Collect the Data

Draw a diagram of the experiment, indicating variables.

Describe the procedure for the experiment.

_____

_____

_____

_____

_____

_____

_____

_____

_____

_____

_____

The independent variable, x, is _____ Units _____

The dependent variable, y, is _____ Units _____

Equipment (labels and measurements)

Tube number _____   Length _____ Diameter _____

Data Collection

Independent _____	Dependent _____		
	Trial 1	Trial 2	Trial 3

Points to Be Graphed

x	y

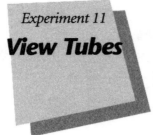

Experiment 11

View Tubes

Name _____

Find the Equation

After plotting your data on graph paper, draw a straight line through two of your points. Choose the line that best fits your data. Circle the points on your graph and copy their coordinates below.

Your points: (____, _____) and (____, _____)

Use these points to find the equation of your line. Show your work.

Find the slope of the line.

Find the *y*-intercept of the line.

Write the equation of the line.

$y =$ _____ $x +$ _____ $y =$ _____ $x +$ _____
rational form   *decimal form*

Rewrite the decimal form of the equation, using the names of the variables instead of *x* and *y*.

_____ = _____ _____ + _____

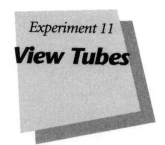

Experiment 11

View Tubes

Name _____

Interpret the Data
Metric Measures

Write the decimal form of your equation here. $y =$ _____ $x +$ _____
Use this equation to answer the questions. Show your work.

1. How much would you see if the distance from the wall were 3.5 meters?

   _____

2. How far from the wall would you have to be to see exactly 57 cm?

   _____

3. How far from the wall would you have to be to see exactly 68 cm?

   _____

4. How would your graph be different if you used a longer tube? _____

   _____

5. How would your graph be different if you used a wider tube? _____

   _____

6. Find some tall object, such as the hall clock, the school flagpole, or the gym door. Measure how far from the object you have to be to see the entire object. Use your equation to estimate the object's height. If possible, verify your measurement.

   Object _____

   Height _____

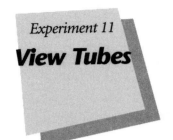

Experiment 11

View Tubes

Name _____

Interpret the Data
Standard Measures

Write the decimal form of your equation here. $y =$ _____ $x +$ _____
Use this equation to answer the questions. Show your work.

1.   How much would you see if the distance from the wall were 10.5 feet?

      _____

2.   How far from the wall would you have to be to see exactly 25 inches?

      _____

3.   How far from the wall would you have to be to see exactly 33 inches?

      _____

4.   How would your graph be different if you used a longer tube? _____

      _____

5.   How would your graph be different if you used a wider tube? _____

      _____

6.   Find some tall object, such as the hall clock, the school flagpole, or the gym
      door. Measure how far from the object you have to be to see the entire
      object. Use your equation to estimate the object's height. If possible, verify
      your measurement.

      Object _____

      Height _____

View Tubes Extension

Teaching Notes

In this experiment, the vertical viewing distance is a linear function of the diameter of the tube. The diameter of the tube is the *independent variable*, and the measure of the viewable vertical distance is the *dependent variable*. The students now hold the distance from the wall and the tube length fixed.

Equipment

assorted tubes, 1 per group

> *Number the tubes. Try to have several tubes of the same length but different diameters, and some of the same diameter but different lengths. Tubes from kitchen wraps (plastic, wax paper, foil) work well. Sawed-off lengths from the core of a carpet or fabric bolt add variety. Cut them long enough so that rolling the eye doesn't distort the measurements.*

metersticks or tape measures, 2 per group

centimeter rulers

> *Used to measure diameters more precisely.*

graph paper, 1 sheet per student

Procedure

Students should use assorted tubes of the same length. Students work in groups of two. Students wearing glasses should not be paired with students who do not.

Reasonable accuracy is obtained if students measure the distance from the toes to the wall.

The vertical viewing distance is a linear function of the independent variable (the diameter). What does the intercept correspond to? For a geometric analysis, see the illustration below.

d: distance to the wall

l: length of the tube

x: diameter of the tube

y: viewable vertical distance

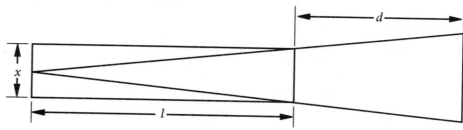

By similar triangles, $\dfrac{\frac{y}{2}}{d+l} = \dfrac{\frac{x}{2}}{l}$, or $y = x + \dfrac{xd}{l} = x\left(1 + \dfrac{d}{l}\right)$

Thus, *y* is a linear function of *x*, where *d* and *l* are fixed values.

View Tubes Extension

Name _____

Partner _____

Collect the Data

Draw a diagram of the experiment, indicating variables.

Describe the procedure for the experiment.

_____

_____

_____

_____

_____

_____

_____

_____

_____

_____

The independent variable, x, is _____   Units _____

The dependent variable, y, is _____   Units _____

Equipment (labels and measurements)

Fixed distance from wall _____   Fixed length of tube _____

Data Collection

Independent _____	Dependent _____		
	Trial 1	Trial 2	Trial 3

Points to Be Graphed

x	y

Experiment 12

View Tubes Extension

Name _____

Find the Equation

After plotting your data on graph paper, draw a straight line through two of your points. Choose the line that best fits your data. Circle the points on your graph and copy their coordinates below.

Your points: (_____, _____) and (_____, _____)

Use these points to find the equation of your line. Show your work.

Find the slope of the line.

Find the *y*-intercept of the line.

Write the equation of the line.

$y =$ _____ $x +$ _____ $y =$ _____ $x +$ _____
                        rational form   *decimal form*

Rewrite the decimal form of the equation, using the names of the variables instead of *x* and *y*.

_____ = _____ _____ + _____

Experiment 12

View Tubes Extension

Name _____

Interpret the Data

Write the decimal form of your equation here. $y =$ _____ $x +$ _____
Use this equation to answer the questions. Show your work.

1. Using the same length of tube and the same distance from the wall, what would the vertical viewing distance be if the diameter were 4 cm?

   _____

2. What would the diameter be if you could see exactly 25 cm? _____

3. What would the diameter be if you could see exactly 45 cm? _____

4. What is the maximum diameter that makes sense for this experiment? _____

   Why? _____

   _____

5. Geoff did the same experiment with a view tube that had a smaller diameter. How would the graph of Geoff's line differ from yours?

   _____

   _____

Experiment 13

Candle Life

Teaching Notes

In this experiment, the duration of a flame is a linear function of the volume of the container. The *independent variable* is the volume of the container, and the *dependent variable* is the time in seconds for the flame to be extinguished once the container has been placed over it.

Equipment

food-warming candles, 1 per class or group

> *About one-half-inch high and in an aluminum case.*

stopwatches, or a watch that displays seconds, 1 per class or group

glass containers of varying sizes (at least 6 different sizes of containers are needed)

> *Number the containers. Find at least 5 different sizes. Containers must be transparent and have flat tops so air cannot enter when they are inverted. Try medium-sized tumblers (about 10 oz.), vases, glass bowls, and carafes.*

measuring cups

> *At least 2-cup size and marked in milliliters.*

water

graph paper, 1 sheet per student

Procedure

You may want to have students observe and measure the times while you alone handle the candle and containers. Students can measure the volumes of the containers, either before or after the timings are taken. If you do the timings first, have students enter the container number in the independent variable column of the Data Collection chart, leaving room for entering the volume later.

Light the candle. Have one student invert the bowl while the other activates the stopwatch. Stop timing when the flame is extinguished (at the instant smoke appears). Repeat with at least 4 different containers.

The best value for this experiment will be the average of two trials for a given volume. The time of burning is a linear function of the volume of air.

Experiment 13

Candle Life

Name _____

Partner _____

Collect the Data

Draw a diagram of the experiment, indicating variables.

Describe the procedure for the experiment.

_____

_____

_____

_____

_____

_____

_____

_____

_____

The independent variable, *x*, is _____ Units _____

The dependent variable, *y*, is _____ Units _____

Containers (numbers and measurements) _____

_____

Data Collection

Independent _____	Dependent _____		
	Trial 1	Trial 2	Trial 3

Points to Be Graphed

x	*y*

Experiment 13

Candle Life

Name _____

Find the Equation

After plotting your data on graph paper, draw a straight line through two of your points. Choose the line that best fits your data. Circle the points on your graph and copy their coordinates below.

Your points: (_____, _____) and (_____, _____)

Use these points to find the equation of your line. Show your work.

Find the slope of the line.

Find the *y*-intercept of the line.

Write the equation of the line.

$y =$ _____ $x +$ _____

rational form

$y =$ _____ $x +$ _____

decimal form

Rewrite the decimal form of the equation, using the names of the variables instead of *x* and *y*.

_____ = _____ _____ + _____

Experiment 13

Candle Life

Name _____

Interpret the Data

Write the decimal form of your equation here. $y =$ _____ $x +$ _____
Use this equation to answer the questions. Show your work.

1. How long would the candle burn if you covered it with a 40-ml container?
    _____

2. Sandra's candle lasted 435 seconds. What size container had she used?
    _____

3. Tom's candle lasted 213 seconds. What size container had he used?
    _____

4. Suppose a room measures 3 meters by 4 meters by 2.5 meters. What is the
    volume of the room in cubic centimeters? _____

    How long would a candle last in this room? _____

5. What conditions could produce a steeper line than yours?

    _____

    _____

Experiment 14

Spilled Ink

Teaching Notes

In this experiment, the diameter of a blot is a linear function of the number of drops. The number of drops is the *independent variable,* and the average diameter of a water spot is the *dependent variable.*

Equipment

straws or medicine droppers, 1 per group

water

food coloring

paper towels

> Use school-quality brown, smooth towels; not especially absorbent. Don't use soft or bumpy towels.

rulers, 1 per group

graph paper, 1 sheet per student

Procedure

This experiment works best if students use a double layer of paper towels. They should try to make small drops of equal size, in the center of the towels, and try not to make spots where the towels have creases. If students use a straw, instruct them to allow gravity to do most of the work in forming the drops. If the water spots are made and measured carefully, the data are approximately linear.

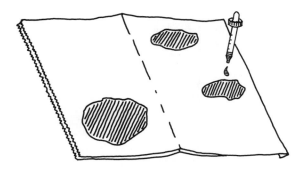

The drops will spread in a circular fashion. It is easiest to make a "pallet" of blots—using 1, 2, 3, and 4 blots—all at once, and then measure them. Blots made from 5 and 6 drops form very large circles; use a separate paper towel for each blot.

The spots should be measured as soon as they have finished spreading. Some spots will be more elliptical than circular. Taking an average of the largest and smallest diameters usually provides usable data.

Experiment 14

Spilled Ink

Name _____

Partner _____

Collect the Data

Draw a diagram of the experiment, indicating variables.

Describe the procedure for the experiment.

_____

_____

_____

_____

_____

_____

_____

_____

_____

The independent variable, *x*, is _____   Units _____

The dependent variable, *y*, is _____   Units _____

Equipment (labels and measurements) _____

Data Collection			Points to Be Graphed	
Independent	Dependent		*x*	*y*
_____	_____			

Experiment 14

Spilled Ink

Name _____

Find the Equation

After plotting your data on graph paper, draw a straight line through two of
your points. Choose the line that best fits your data. Circle the points on your
graph and copy their coordinates below.

Your points: (____, _____) and (____, _____)

Use these points to find the equation of your line. Show your work.

Find the slope of the line.

Find the *y*-intercept of the line.

Write the equation of the line.

$y =$ _____ $x +$ _____ $y =$ _____ $x +$ _____
          rational form   *decimal form*

Rewrite the decimal form of the equation, using the names of the variables instead of *x* and *y*.

_____ $=$ _____ _____ $+$ _____

Spilled Ink

Name _____

Interpret the Data
Metric Measures

Write the decimal form of your equation here. $y =$ _____ $x +$ _____
Use this equation to answer the questions. Show your work.

1. Suppose you were to use 10 drops (and the paper towel did not dissolve).
    What would be the diameter of the circle formed? _____

2. How many drops would be needed to form a circle of diameter 27 cm?

    _____

3. How many drops would be needed to form a circle of diameter 38 cm?

    _____

4. How would your graph change if you were to use larger drops?

    _____

    _____

Experiment 14
Spilled Ink

Name _____

Interpret the Data
Standard Measures

Write the decimal form of your equation here. $y =$ _____ $x +$ _____
Use this equation to answer the questions. Show your work.

1. Suppose you were to use 10 drops (and the paper towel did not dissolve).
    What would be the diameter of the circle formed? _____

2. How many drops would be needed to form a circle of diameter 11 inches?
    _____

3. How many drops would be needed to form a circle of diameter 15 inches?
    _____

4. How would your graph change if you were to use larger drops?

    _____

    _____

Sum of the Angles

Teaching Notes

In this experiment, the sum of the interior angles of a polygon is a linear function of the number of sides in the polygon. The number of sides is the *independent variable*, and the sum of the angles is the *dependent variable*. Students of all abilities seem to enjoy creating their own polygons and measuring the angles.

Equipment

straightedges, 1 per student

circular protractors, 1 per student

> *We suggest making several copies of the blackline master on overhead-transparency sheets. Mark the center dot and the 0-degree line in color. Students find the thin transparencies easier to use than actual protractors.*

angle copiers (optional)

> *After making a copy on a transparency, cut out the circular part. With a razor blade, cut the semi-circular tabs. Slide the circle under the tabs. The circular part should turn freely. Mark the stationary line in color. Some students prefer to "copy" the angle and then measure the copy.*

calculators, 1 per group

scratch paper, a large amount

graph paper, 1 sheet per student

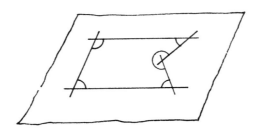

Procedure

Have each student use a straightedge to draw an acute angle, mark the angle, and then measure it with a protractor. (Don't begin by passing out a page of angles to be measured; it is important that students draw and mark each angle.) Measuring to the nearest degree is sufficiently accurate. Lines of angles should cross; otherwise, there is a tendency to fill in the gap freehand. This may drastically affect the measurement of the angle.

After successfully measuring several acute angles, have students draw and measure some reflex angles.

Groups of three work particularly well with this experiment. Starting with a 4-sided polygon, each student draws a polygon; the number of sides is the *independent variable*. Next, each student measures the interior angles, lists the measurements, and finds their sum, the *dependent variable*. At least one of the polygons should be "fancy," that is, shaped like an arrowhead (containing a reflex angle).

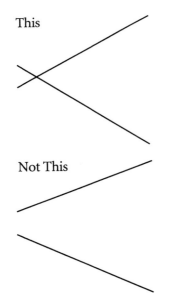

This

Not This

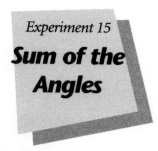

Experiment 15

Sum of the Angles

Teaching Notes, page 2

Calculators are essential to add the angles. If one student's results vary widely from the others in the group, the mistake could be a faulty measurement, the omission of an angle, or the miscounting of the number of sides. Listing the angles to be added and then using the calculator minimizes addition mistakes.

Then, group members enter their data for the 4-sided polygon and take either the average or the middle value. Starting with a polygon of 4 sides is suggested because some students may remember the formula for the sum of the angles of a triangle. Repeat for polygons with 5, 6, 7, 8, and 9 sides. When plotting their points, students will need a large scale for the y-axis.

Extension

Ask students what their equations predict for the sum of the angles in a triangle. Take an average of the answers.

A class average of the slopes and intercepts should produce a line very nearly the theoretical equation of

$$y = 180x - 360.$$

Ask: What is the meaning of the intercept? There are no 0-sided polygons. In the other experiments, it made sense to consider all positive values of the independent variable. Here it makes sense to consider only (integer) values greater than 2.

A square (or any 4-sided polygon) can be cut into two triangles. What is the minimum number of triangles a 5-sided figure can be cut into? The independent variable is the number of sides, the dependent variable is the minimum number of triangles. Students can use their old polygons or draw new ones. The result is linear.

Circular Protractors

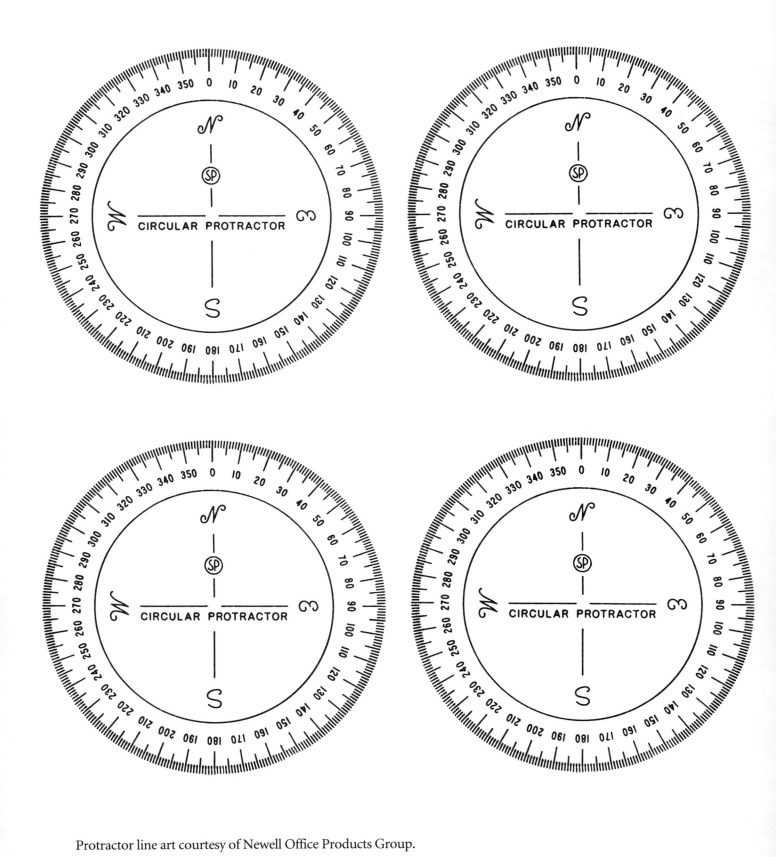

Protractor line art courtesy of Newell Office Products Group.

Angle Copiers

After making a copy on a transparency, cut out the circular part. With a razor blade, cut the semi-circular tabs. Slide the circle under the tabs. The circular part should turn freely. Mark the stationary line in color.

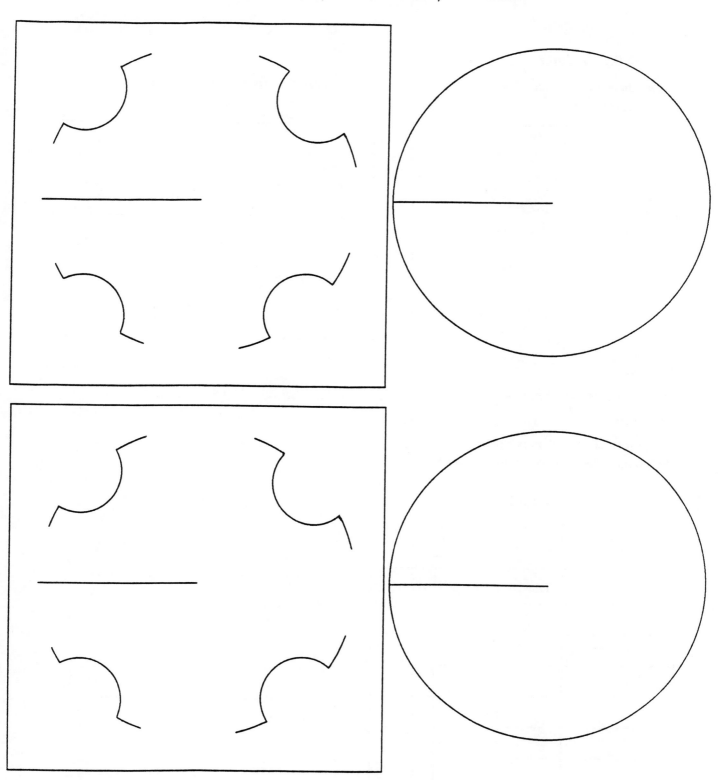

Experiment 15

Sum of the Angles

Name _____

Partner _____

Collect the Data

Draw a diagram of the experiment, indicating variables.

Describe the procedure for the experiment.

_____

_____

_____

_____

_____

_____

_____

_____

_____

_____

The independent variable, x, is _____ Units _____

The dependent variable, y, is _____ Units _____

Equipment (labels and measurements) _____
Please attach the paper with your polygons.

Data Collection

	Dependent		
Independent _____	_____		
	Trial 1	Trial 2	Trial 3

Points to Be Graphed

x	y

Experiment 15

Sum of the Angles

Name _____

Find the Equation

After plotting your data on graph paper, draw a straight line through two of your points. Choose the line that best fits your data. Circle the points on your graph and copy their coordinates below.

Your points: (_____, _____) and (_____, _____)

Use these points to find the equation of your line. Show your work.

Find the slope of the line.

Find the *y*-intercept of the line.

Write the equation of the line.

$y =$ _____ $x +$ _____ $y =$ _____ $x +$ _____
                rational form   *decimal form*

Rewrite the decimal form of the equation, using the names of the variables instead of *x* and *y*.

_____ = _____ _____ + _____

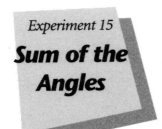

Experiment 15

Sum of the Angles

Name _____

Interpret the Data

Write the decimal form of your equation here. $y =$ _____ $x +$ _____
Use this equation to answer the questions. Show your work.

1. What would be the sum of the angles for a polygon with 12 sides?

    _____

2. How many sides would be needed to have the sum of the angles be 2160°?

    _____

3. How many sides would be needed to have the sum of the angles be 2530°?

    _____

4. On the back of your graph, draw a polygon with 12 sides that has all square angles. Try: ⊏

    What is the sum of the angles for this polygon? _____

    Does it match the answer from your equation? _____

5. Does it make sense to have values for the independent variable less than 3? Why or why not?

    _____

Experiment 16

Circles

Teaching Notes

In this experiment, the circumference of a circle is a linear function of its diameter. The diameter of the circle is the *independent variable,* and the circumference of the circle is the *dependent variable.* If this experiment is done as a class activity, each group of two students selects one object and measures its diameter and circumference.

Equipment

cloth tape measures, or ruler and string, 1 per group

The string should have no stretch to it.

scratch paper

scissors, 1 pair per group

round objects, such as cans and jar lids, 1 per group

graph paper, 1 sheet per student

Procedure

If the activity is done as a whole-class activity, have half the groups measure in centimeters, the other half in inches. Keep the two data points separate; at the end of the experiment you may want to compare their equations and graphs.

To find the diameter of the objects, have students trace around each object, cut out the circle, fold it exactly in half, and measure the length of the crease. They can measure circumference either by wrapping a cloth tape measure around the object, or by wrapping a string around the object and measuring the string.

Organizing and Analyzing Class Results

List the decimal equations for each of the groups. For each group, ask questions such as: Who used centimeters? Who used inches? Can you tell from the graphs? From the equations?

The line(s) drawn should have slope between 2.9 and 3.3. If any students find a non-zero intercept, discuss why this might have occurred. *Ask:* In theory, what's the circumference of a circle with diameter 0? Why did your data lead to a non-zero intercept?

At the end of this experiment, discuss the definition of π.

Name _____

Partner _____

Collect the Data

Draw a diagram of the experiment, indicating variables.

Describe the procedure for the experiment.

_____

_____

_____

_____

_____

_____

_____

_____

The independent variable, x, is _____ Units _____

The dependent variable, y, is _____ Units _____

Equipment (labels and measurements) _____

_____

Data Collection	
Independent	Dependent
_____	_____

Points to Be Graphed	
x	y

Experiment 16

Circles

Name _____

Find the Equation

After plotting your data on graph paper, draw a straight line through two of
your points. Choose the line that best fits your data. Circle the points on your
graph and copy their coordinates below.

Your points: (____ , _____) and (____ , _____)

Use these points to find the equation of your line. Show your work.

Find the slope of the line.

Find the *y*-intercept of the line.

Write the equation of the line.

$y =$ _____ $x +$ _____ $y =$ _____ $x +$ _____
          rational form   *decimal form*

Rewrite the decimal form of the equation, using the names of the variables instead of *x* and *y*.

_____ = _____ _____ + _____

Experiment 16

Circles

Name _____

Interpret the Data
Metric Measures

Write the decimal form of your equation here. $y =$ _____ $x +$ _____
Use this equation to answer the first four questions. Show your work.

1.   What is the circumference of a circle with a diameter of 33 cm?
     _____

2.   What is the diameter of a circle with a circumference of 350 cm?
     _____

3.   What is the diameter of a circle with a circumference of 93 cm?
     _____

4.   According to your equation, what is the diameter of a circle with a circum-
     ference of 360 cm (10 cm more than the circle in Question 2)?
     _____

5.   Measure the circumference of a tree. What is its diameter? _____

6.   Otis measured large objects and used meters instead of centimeters for
     both variables. What effect would this have on the resulting equation and
     graph?

     _____

     _____

Experiment 16
Circles

Name _____

Interpret the Data
Standard Measures

Write the decimal form of your equation here. $y =$ _____ $x +$ _____
Use this equation to answer the first four questions. Show your work.

1.   What is the circumference of a circle with a diameter of 14 inches?

_____

2.   What is the diameter of a circle with a circumference of 150 inches?

_____

3.   What is the diameter of a circle with a circumference of 42 inches?

_____

4.   According to your equation, what is the diameter of a circle with a circum-
      ference of 160 inches (10 inches more than the circle in Question 2)?

_____

5.   Measure the circumference of a tree. What is its diameter? _____

6.   Otis measured large objects and used feet instead of inches for both
      variables. What effect would this have on the resulting equation and
      graph?

      _____

      _____

Experiment 17
Cube Faces

Teaching Notes

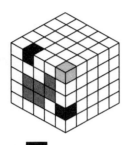

 2 sides

 3 sides

 1 side

In this experiment, students build a large cube using sugar cubes. The number of cubes on an edge of the large cube is the *independent variable,* and the number of sugar cubes with exactly two faces to the outside of the large cube is the *dependent variable.*

Equipment

    sugar cubes or small, individual blocks

    washable felt-tip markers, 1 per group

    graph paper, 1 sheet per student

Procedure

Have each group of two students make a 6 by 6 by 6 cube from individual sugar cubes. The number of cubes on an edge is the *independent variable* (in this case, 6).

Students mark all of the outside faces of the cube with the markers. Next, they take the cube apart and count the number of sugar cubes with exactly two sides marked. This value is the *dependent variable.*

Next, they bury the marked sugar cubes inside a new construction to build a clean 5 by 5 by 5 cube, then repeat the process for 4 by 4 by 4, 3 by 3 by 3, and 2 by 2 by 2 cubes.

Extension

If students have experience with higher-degree equations, suggest that they investigate letting the dependent variable be either the number of cubes with no sides marked or the number of cubes with exactly one side marked.

Cube Faces

Name _____

Partner _____

Collect the Data

Draw a diagram of the experiment, indicating variables.

Describe the procedure for the experiment.

The independent variable, x, is _____ Units _____

The dependent variable, y, is _____ Units _____

Data Collection	
Independent	Dependent

Points to Be Graphed	
x	y

Experiment 17

Cube Faces

Name _____

Find the Equation

After plotting your data on graph paper, draw a straight line through two of your points. Choose the line that best fits your data. Circle the points on your graph and copy their coordinates below.

Your points: (_____, _____) and (_____, _____)

Use these points to find the equation of your line. Show your work.

Find the slope of the line.

Find the *y*-intercept of the line.

Write the equation of the line.

$y =$ _____ $x +$ _____ $y =$ _____ $x +$ _____
            rational form   *decimal form*

Rewrite the decimal form of the equation, using the names of the variables instead of *x* and *y*.

_____ = _____ _____ + _____

Experiment 17

Cube Faces

Name _____

Interpret the Data

Write the decimal form of your equation here. $y =$ _____ $x +$ _____
Use this equation to answer the questions. Show your work.

1. How many blocks would have exactly 2 sides marked if your cube were
    10 blocks on an edge? _____

2. How many blocks would be needed for the edge of a cube if there were
    216 blocks with 2 sides marked? _____

3. How many blocks would have exactly 3 sides marked if your cube were
    10 blocks on an edge? _____

Experiment _____   Name _____